Look! Listen! Think!

Grades 4-5

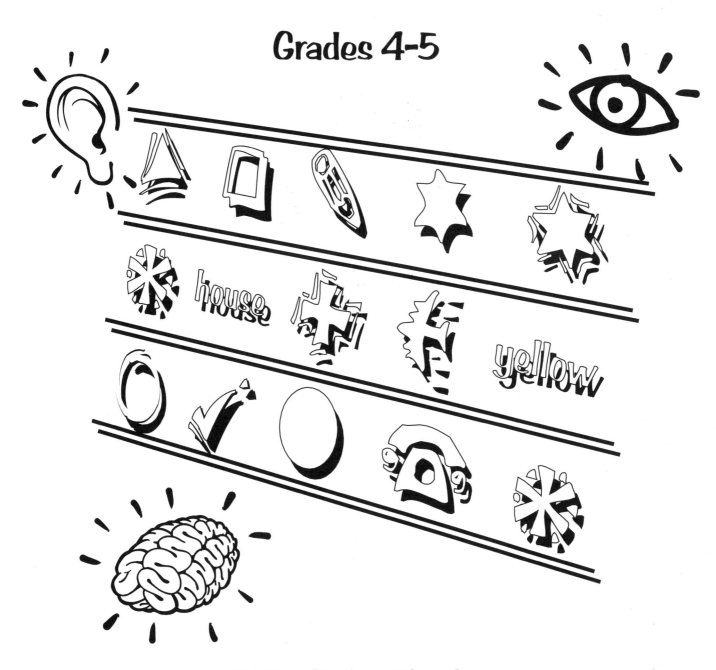

Written By Jean Edwards

Published By World Teachers Press®

Order Number 2-5095
ISBN 1-58324-017-9

B C D E F 99 00 01 02

Educational Resources

395 Main Street
Rowley, MA 01969

Foreword ◀▮▮▮

Look! Listen! Think! is a series of three books designed to provide you with activities to exercise the minds of your students.

Each book contains a series of developmental activities in the following areas:

(i)   Visual discrimination and memory skills—being able to remember what they have seen and answer questions accordingly; and

(ii) Listening comprehension and memory skills—being able to remember what they have heard and follow oral instructions correctly.

Both sections provide you with detailed information to ensure the procedures are easy to follow and administer. Sections can be tackled in any order, but the activities within each section gradually become more difficult, so should be used from set one through to the final set.

Contents ◀▮▮▮

Teacher Information...

...Visual Memory Skills ◀▥

- Distribute the picture to students. It may be cut off separately or the question side may be folded back.

- Students study picture for a time you specify. (Suggestion – forty-five seconds for grades four and five.)

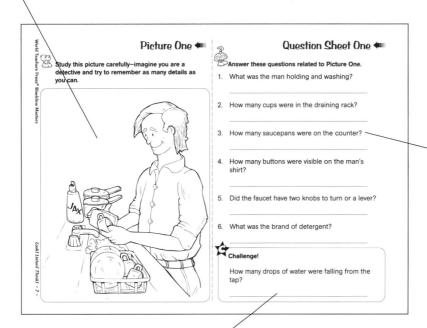

Picture One ◀▥

Study this picture carefully—imagine you are a detective and try to remember as many details as you can.

Question Sheet One ◀▥

Answer these questions related to Picture One.

1. What was the man holding and washing?

2. How many cups were in the draining rack?

3. How many saucepans were on the counter?

4. How many buttons were visible on the man's shirt?

5. Did the faucet have two knobs to turn or a lever?

6. What was the brand of detergent?

★ Challenge!

How many drops of water were falling from the tap?

- Picture is turned over.

- Students answer questions. You may read questions if there are reading difficulties.

- Activity may also be given verbally on an individual basis with you writing the responses.

- Challenge! is answered but not recorded on scoring sheet.

- Distribute a scoring sheet from page 13 to each student.

- Scores can be recorded by:

  (a) students individually checking the picture;

  (b) teacher marking individually; or

  (c) teacher discussing answers with the whole class.

- Do not ask the students to call out their score unless they are comfortable with this approach.

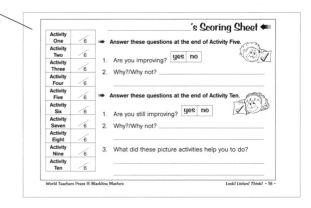

's Scoring Sheet ◀▥

Activity One	/6
Activity Two	/6
Activity Three	/6
Activity Four	/6
Activity Five	/6
Activity Six	/6
Activity Seven	/6
Activity Eight	/6
Activity Nine	/6
Activity Ten	/6

➡ Answer these questions at the end of Activity Five.

1. Are you improving? yes no

2. Why?/Why not? _____

➡ Answer these questions at the end of Activity Ten.

1. Are you still improving? yes no

2. Why?/Why not? _____

3. What did these picture activities help you to do? _____

Teacher Information...

...Listening Memory Skills ◀▥▥

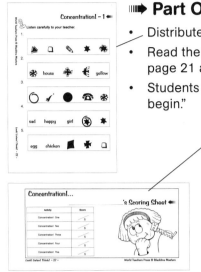

▥▶ Part One – Concentration!

- Distribute the student activity page.
- Read the instructions from teacher copy on page 21 and 22..
- Students complete each row after you say, "You may begin."

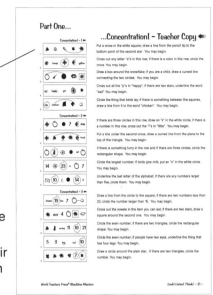

- Distribute a scoring sheet from page 28 to each student.
- Scores can be recorded by:
  (a) teacher marking individually; or
  (b) teacher discussing answers with the whole class.
- Do not ask the students to call out their score unless they are comfortable with this approach.

▥▶ Part Two – Item Missing

- Distribute a scoring sheet from page 32 to each student.

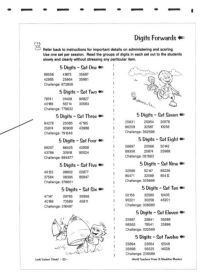

- Administer "Item Missing" activities to students from pages 30 and 31.

- Student writes missing item on scoring sheet.
- Supply the answers and students record their score.
- Do not ask students to call out their score unless they are comfortable with this approach.

▥▶ Parts Three and Four – Digits Forwards and Digits Backwards

- Distribute a scoring sheet from page 36 or 40 to each student.
- Administer the "Digits Forwards" activities from pages 34 and 35, and "Digits Backwards" activities from pages 38 and 39.
- Student writes the sequence of digits on the scoring sheet whether it be forwards or backwards.

- Supply the answers and students record their score.
- Do not ask students to call out their score unless they are comfortable with this approach.
- Challenge! is answered on the sheet but not recorded in the total.

Visual discrimination and visual memory skills form an integral part of many daily activities. They are essential and critical skill areas, but we don't often, or regularly, teach or consciously develop them in our classroom program.

Visual discrimination and visual memory skills can be enhanced by practice and your students will benefit from regular exercises at least once a week. These activities will help to provide that practice.

You can explain to your students that the mind is rather like a muscle, in that it can be exercised and strengthened and that these activities are designed to provide that exercise.

The illustrations on the following pages are to help improve visual discrimination and visual memory skills. The activities become gradually more difficult.

The pages have been designed to be used in two ways:

1. You can cut the page down the middle and distributes the picture. The students turn the illustration over after studying it and you read the questions.

2. The students fold the page down the middle and study the picture side. Then they turn it over to answer the questions without being able to see the picture. Be sure students do not read the questions before studying the picture.

In this section students are required to remember what they have seen in the picture and answer questions accordingly.

Instructions

⟹ Tell the students that the activity is to help them with their visual memory—remembering details of what they have seen. (Like playing detective.)

⟹ Distribute a copy of the illustration to each student and allow them a stated time to scan the illustration; for example, forty-five seconds for students in grades four and five.

⟹ Turn the illustration over and answer the questions on the answer sheet—this allows students to work at their own pace.

⟹ You can also read the questions, allowing suitable time for answering if there are reading difficulties.

⟹ The activity can also be given verbally on an individual basis, with you writing down the student's responses.

Scoring

⟹ Students can mark their own work, by checking the illustration, or you can discuss the answers with the students.

⟹ Students enter their score on the scoring sheet provided on page 18.

Question Sheet One

Answer these questions related to Picture One.

1. What was the man holding and washing?

2. How many cups were in the draining rack?

3. How many saucepans were on the counter?

4. How many buttons were visible on the man's shirt?

5. Did the faucet have two knobs to turn or a lever?

6. What was the brand of detergent?

 **Challenge!**

How many drops of water were falling from the faucet?

Picture One

Study this picture carefully—imagine you are a detective and try to remember as many details as you can.

Answer these questions related to Picture Two.

1. What was lying on the ground underneath the slide?

2. Was the boy coming down the slide holding on with his hands?

3. Who was wearing a hat?

4. Who was wearing shorts?

5. How many legs were holding up the lower end of the slide?

6. How many steps were on the ladder?

Challenge!

Which foot did the girl have on the step?

Picture Two ◄▐▐▐

Study this picture carefully—imagine you are a detective and try to remember as many details as you can.

Question Sheet Three

 **Answer these questions related to Picture Three.**

1. Was the woman wearing earrings?

2. How many sausages were on the barbecue?

3. In which hand was the man holding the tongs?

4. What did the man have on his feet?

5. Was the woman wearing socks?

6. What was the name on the barbecue?

 Challenge!

Was the man wearing a shirt with or without a collar?

Picture Three

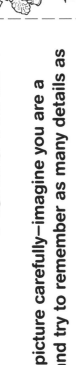 **Study this picture carefully–imagine you are a detective and try to remember as many details as you can.**

HOT SIZZLE

Question Sheet Four ◀▥

Answer these questions related to Picture Four.

1. What caused the flat tire?

2. Was it the front or the back wheel that was punctured?

3. Was the girl's hair dark or light?

4. Was one of the tools on the ground a hammer?

5. What item was on the ground along with the tools?

6. How many bolts were on the ground?

Challenge!
Did the girl have a collar on her clothes?

Picture Four ◀▥

Study this picture carefully–imagine you are a detective and try to remember as many details as you can.

Question Sheet Five ◀▥

Answer these questions related to Picture Five.

1. What was in the sink?

_____

2. What could you see out the window?

_____

3. Where was the vase of flowers?

_____

4. How many containers were there altogether on the left of the sink?

_____

5. What was leaning against the kitchen cupboards?

_____

6. What time was it on the clock?

_____

Challenge!

Was there the same amount of cupboards and drawers?

_____

Picture Five ◀▥

Study this picture carefully—imagine you are a detective and try to remember as many details as you can.

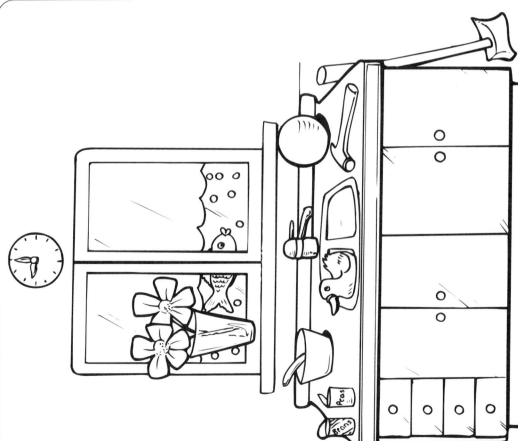

Question Sheet Six

 **Answer these questions related to Picture Six.**

1. How many people were in the picture?

2. Did the mother have light or dark hair?

3. What was under the table?

4. Name the item the mother was holding in her hand.

5. How many places were set on the table?

6. Was there a tablecloth on the table?

Challenge!
Was the woman wearing a skirt or a dress?

Picture Six

 Study this picture carefully–imagine you are a detective and try to remember as many details as you can.

World Teachers Press®

Question Sheet Seven

Answer these questions related to Picture Seven.

1. Did the salesperson have light or dark hair?

2. Was the salesperson wearing glasses?

3. Did the mother have a purse?

4. What was in the small container between the salesperson and the mother?

5. Was the mother wearing shoes with heels?

6. Who was taller—the salesperson or the mother?

Challenge!

How many buttons could you see on the mother's coat?

Picture Seven

Study this picture carefully—imagine you are a detective and try to remember as many details as you can.

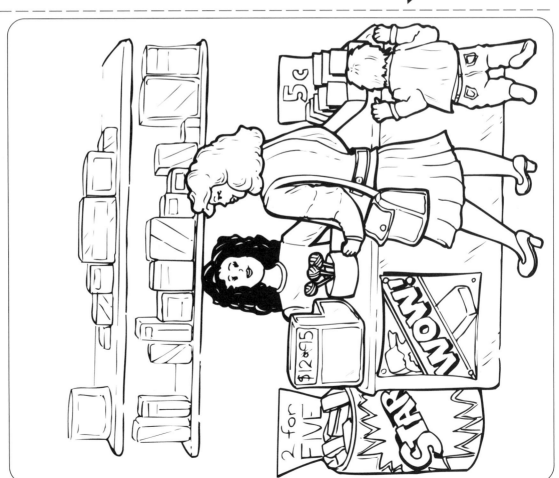

Question Sheet Eight

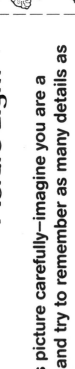

Answer these questions related to Picture Eight.

1. How many lily pads were in the pond?

2. What were the boys sitting under the tree doing?

3. Was the person rollerblading wearing a helmet?

4. How many flowers were there in the park?

5. How many animals were in the pond?

6. Was there a nest in the tree?

Challenge!

How many birds were sitting in the tree?

Picture Eight

Study this picture carefully–imagine you are a detective and try to remember as many details as you can.

World Teachers Press®

Question Sheet Nine

Answer these questions related to Picture Nine.

1. How many balloons were in the picture?

_____

2. How old was the birthday person?

_____

3. How many boys are in the picture?

_____

4. What food was on the table?

_____

5. What was the pattern on the wrapping paper of the large gift?

_____

6. How many children were holding balloons?

_____

Challenge!

Was the table round or square?

_____

Picture Nine

Study this picture carefully–imagine you are a detective and try to remember as many details as you can.

Question Sheet Ten

Answer these questions related to Picture Ten.

1. What was the design on the girl's bathing suit?

2. How many people were wearing a hat?

3. What was the adult doing?

4. Could you see the sailing boy's hands?

5. What item was next to the boy with the surfboard?

6. Was the adult wearing glasses?

Challenge!

Was the adult wearing a shirt with a collar?

Picture Ten

Study this picture carefully—imagine you are a detective and try to remember as many details as you can.

World Teachers Press®

Answers...

Picture One – Page 7
1. a cup
2. two
3. two
4. three
5. two knobs
6. JAX

☆ two

Picture Two – Page 8
1. book, apple
2. no
3. boy on slide
4. boy on slide
5. four
6. three

☆ left

Picture Three – Page 9
1. yes
2. nine
3. right
4. sandals/scuffs/thongs
5. yes
6. HOT SIZZLE

☆ with a collar

Picture Four – Page 10
1. nail/tack
2. front
3. dark
4. yes
5. bucket
6. two

☆ yes

Picture Five – Page 11
1. duck
2. fish/water
3. on the sill
4. three
5. axe
6. 9 o'clock

☆ yes

Picture Six – Page 12
1. three
2. dark
3. dog
4. pitcher
5. four
6. yes

☆ dress

Picture Seven – Page 13
1. dark
2. no
3. yes
4. lollipops
5. yes
6. mother

☆ one

Picture Eight – Page 14
1. three
2. reading
3. yes
4. two
5. one
6. no

☆ two

Picture Nine – Page 15
1. five
2. ten
3. two
4. chips, cupcakes, birthday cake
5. spots/dots
6. two

☆ round

Picture Ten – Page 16
1. spots/dots
2. two
3. reading
4. no
5. cooler
6. yes

☆ no

_____ 's Scoring Sheet ◀▮▮▮

Activity One	/ 6
Activity Two	/ 6
Activity Three	/ 6
Activity Four	/ 6
Activity Five	/ 6
Activity Six	/ 6
Activity Seven	/ 6
Activity Eight	/ 6
Activity Nine	/ 6
Activity Ten	/ 6

▮▮▶ **Answer these questions at the end of Activity Five.**

1. Are you improving? | yes | no |

2. Why?/Why not? _____

_____

▮▮▶ **Answer these questions at the end of Activity Ten.**

1. Are you still improving? | yes | no |

2. Why?/Why not? _____

_____

3. What did these picture activities help you to do?

_____

_____

_____ 's Scoring Sheet ◀▮▮▮

Activity One	/ 6
Activity Two	/ 6
Activity Three	/ 6
Activity Four	/ 6
Activity Five	/ 6
Activity Six	/ 6
Activity Seven	/ 6
Activity Eight	/ 6
Activity Nine	/ 6
Activity Ten	/ 6

▮▮▶ **Answer these questions at the end of Activity Five.**

1. Are you improving? | yes | no |

2. Why?/Why not? _____

_____

▮▮▶ **Answer these questions at the end of Activity Ten.**

1. Are you still improving? | yes | no |

2. Why?/Why not? _____

_____

3. What did these picture activities help you to do?

_____

_____

World Teachers Press®

Listening Memory Skills

Listening and memory skills form an integral part of many daily activities, such as reading, spelling, writing and mathematics.

They are essential and critical skill areas that are not often isolated for specific development and attention in our classroom programs.

Listening and memory skills can be enhanced by practice, and your students will benefit from regular exercises at least once a week. These activities will help to provide that practice. They are structured to provide your students with practice in auditory memory, auditory discrimination, memory and concentration skills.

You can explain to your students that the mind is rather like a muscle, in that it can be exercised and strengthened and that these activities are designed to provide that exercise.

The activities in this section are divided into the following subsections:

➠ Concentration!–*listening, concentration and memory*

➠ Item Missing–*listening and memory*

➠ Digits Forwards–*listening and memory*

➠ Digits Backwards–*listening, concentration and memory*

The subsections may be used in any order, however, the sequences within each subsection are in ascending order of difficulty, and it is recommended that you follow them through in their entirety.

Part One...

...Concentration!

In this section, students are required to listen carefully to oral instructions and complete the activity.

The *Concentration!* activities in this section gradually become more complex. Therefore, it is suggested that you work through the activities in the order they are presented. The activities are designed to develop listening, concentration and memory skills with an emphasis on concentration.

Instructions

▶ Tell the students that this activity is designed to help them practice and sharpen their concentration skills. You are going to read a sentence telling them things they can do with each row of pictures or symbols, so they need to listen carefully. You will not be repeating any of the instructions, so they need to listen and concentrate as best they can.

▶ Tell the students that you are going to do the whole page, one row at a time.

▶ Ask them not to make any noise or ask any questions once you have begun, otherwise, they might distract someone else who is trying hard to concentrate.

▶ Tell the students that you are going to read the instructions for each row of symbols. The students are to listen and refrain from working until they hear you say, "You may begin."

▶ Once you have finished giving the instructions, the students then try to remember what you have said and do their work on their activity sheet. Stress that students are not to begin working until you have said, "You may begin."

   NOTE: Tell your students that if they copy the work of others here, it is defeating only themselves as they won't be training themselves to be better listeners. Being honest with themselves here sets them up for success with more difficult sets in the future.

▶ When you are ready to begin, read aloud each instruction slowly, deliberately and clearly. Give the students ample time to complete each row before moving on to the next. Use one activity sheet per session. The activity has been copied twice on the page to reduce the amount of photocopying you need to do.

Scoring

▶ Use the answers on the *Teacher Copy* (pages 21 and 22) to correct the students' work. Record scores on the scoring sheet on page 28.

▶ NOTE: The scoring sheets are designed so students can monitor their own individual progress—they are not designed to compare scores with anyone else. Please avoid asking the students to call their scores aloud in front of the class unless the students say they are quite comfortable with this. You may collect totals individually instead.

Part One...

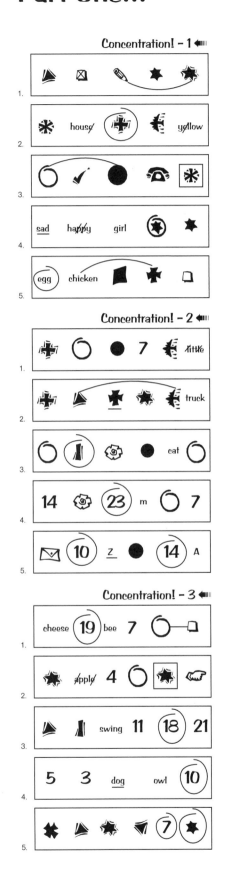

Put an "x" in the white square; draw a line from the pencil tip to the bottom point of the second star. You may begin.

Cross out any letter "e"s in this row; if there is a color in this row, circle the cross. You may begin.

Draw a box around the snowflake; if you are a child, draw a curved line connecting the two circles. You may begin.

Cross out all the "p"s in "happy;" if there are two stars, underline the word "sad." You may begin.

Circle the thing that birds lay; if there is something between the squares, draw a line from it to the word "chicken." You may begin.

If there are three circles in this row, draw an "x" in the white circle, if there is a number in this row, cross out the "l"s in "little." You may begin.

Put a line under the second cross; draw a curved line from the plane to the top of the triangle. You may begin.

If there is something furry in the row and if there are three circles, circle the rectangular shape. You may begin.

Circle the largest number; if birds give milk, put an "s" in the white circle. You may begin.

Underline the last letter of the alphabet; if there are any numbers larger than five, circle them. You may begin.

Draw a line from the circle to the square; if there are two numbers less than twenty, circle the number larger than fifteen. You may begin.

Cross out the vowels in the item you can eat; if there are two stars, draw a square around the second one. You may begin.

Circle the even number; if there are two triangles, circle the rectangular shape. You may begin.

Circle the even number; if people have two eyes, underline the thing that has four legs. You may begin.

Draw a circle around the plain star; if there are two triangles, circle the number. You may begin.

Part One...

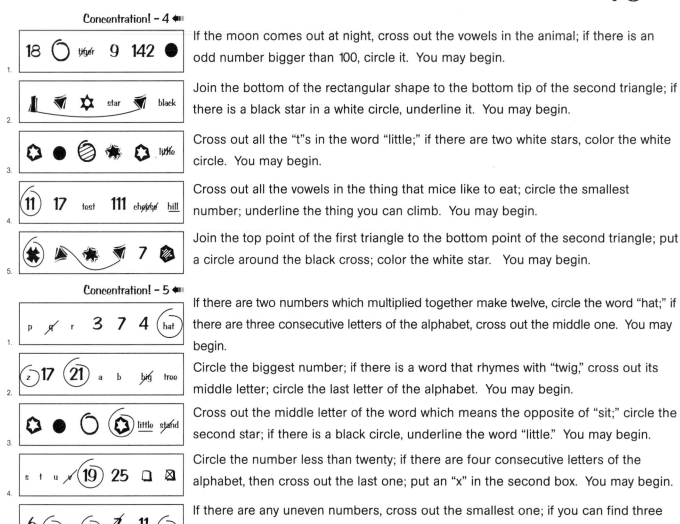

Concentration! – 4 ◀||

1. 18 ◯ ti̶g̶e̶r̶ 9 142 ●

2. (shapes with joining line) ▼ ✿ star ▼ black

3. ✪ ● (striped star) ★ ✪ li̶t̶t̶le

4. (11) 17 test 111 ch̶ee̶s̶e̶ hill

5. (star) ▲ ★ ▼ 7 (hexagon)

Concentration! – 5 ◀||

1. p ʠ̶ r 3 7 4 (hat)

2. (z)17 (21) a b bi̶g tree

3. ✪ ● ◯ (✪) li̶t̶tle sta̶nd

4. s t u ✓(19) 25 ▢ ⊠

5. 6 (s) a (t) ʠ̶ 11 (u)

If the moon comes out at night, cross out the vowels in the animal; if there is an odd number bigger than 100, circle it. You may begin.

Join the bottom of the rectangular shape to the bottom tip of the second triangle; if there is a black star in a white circle, underline it. You may begin.

Cross out all the "t"s in the word "little;" if there are two white stars, color the white circle. You may begin.

Cross out all the vowels in the thing that mice like to eat; circle the smallest number; underline the thing you can climb. You may begin.

Join the top point of the first triangle to the bottom point of the second triangle; put a circle around the black cross; color the white star. You may begin.

If there are two numbers which multiplied together make twelve, circle the word "hat;" if there are three consecutive letters of the alphabet, cross out the middle one. You may begin.

Circle the biggest number; if there is a word that rhymes with "twig," cross out its middle letter; circle the last letter of the alphabet. You may begin.

Cross out the middle letter of the word which means the opposite of "sit;" circle the second star; if there is a black circle, underline the word "little." You may begin.

Circle the number less than twenty; if there are four consecutive letters of the alphabet, then cross out the last one; put an "x" in the second box. You may begin.

If there are any uneven numbers, cross out the smallest one; if you can find three consecutive letters of the alphabet, circle them. You may begin.

        World Teachers Press®

Concentration! – 1 ←

Listen carefully to your teacher.

1.

2. house   yellow

3.

4. sad   happy   girl

5. egg   chicken

Concentration! – 1 ←

Listen carefully to your teacher.

1.

2. house   yellow

3.

4. sad   happy   girl

5. egg   chicken

🐭 Listen carefully to your teacher.

1. ✚ ◯ ● 7 🦇 little

2. ✚ ◢ ✸ ✦ 🦇 truck

3. ◯ ▱ 🌼 ● cat ◯

4. 14 🌼 23 m ◯ 7

5. ✉ 10 z ● 14 ᐱ

Concentration! – 2 ⬇||||

🐭 Listen carefully to your teacher.

1. ✚ ◯ ● 7 🦇 little

2. ✚ ◢ ✸ ✦ 🦇 truck

3. ◯ ▱ 🌼 ● cat ◯

4. 14 🌼 23 m ◯ 7

5. ✉ 10 z ● 14 ᐱ

World Teachers Press®

Concentration! – 3

Listen carefully to your teacher.

1. cheese 19 bee 7

2. apple 4

3. swing 11 18 21

4. 5 3 dog owl 10

5.   7

Concentration! – 3

Listen carefully to your teacher.

1. cheese 19 bee 7

2. apple 4

3. swing 11 18 21

4. 5 3 dog owl 10

5.   7

Concentration! – 4 ◀▏▎▍

👂 Listen carefully to your teacher.

1. | 18 | ⭕ | tiger | 9 | 142 | ● |

2. | ◁ | ▽ | ✡ | star | ▽ | black |

3. | ✪ | ⭕ | ● | ✪ | ✪ | little |

4. | 11 | 17 | test | 111 | cheese | hill |

5. | ✺ | ◁ | ✪ | ✪ | ▽ | 7 | ✪ |

Concentration! – 4 ◀▏▎▍

👂 Listen carefully to your teacher.

1. | 18 | ⭕ | tiger | 9 | 142 | ● |

2. | ◁ | ▽ | ✡ | star | ▽ | black |

3. | ✪ | ⭕ | ● | ✪ | ✪ | little |

4. | 11 | 17 | test | 111 | cheese | hill |

5. | ✺ | ◁ | ✪ | ✪ | ▽ | 7 | ✪ |

Look! Listen! Think! – 26 –

World Teachers Press®

Listen carefully to your teacher.

1. p q r 3 7 4 hat

2. z 17 21 a b big tree

3. ⭐ ● ◯ ☆ little stand

4. s t u v 19 25 ▢ ▢ ▢

5. 6 s a t 7 11 u

Concentration! – 5 ◄▐▐▐

Listen carefully to your teacher.

1. p q r 3 7 4 hat

2. z 17 21 a b big tree

3. ⭐ ● ◯ ☆ little stand

4. s t u v 19 25 ▢ ▢ ▢

5. 6 s a t 7 11 u

Concentration!...

_____ 's Scoring Sheet ◀|||

Activity	Score
Concentration! One	/ 5
Concentration! Two	/ 5
Concentration! Three	/ 5
Concentration! Four	/ 5
Concentration! Five	/ 5

Concentration!...

_____ 's Scoring Sheet ◀|||

Activity	Score
Concentration! One	/ 5
Concentration! Two	/ 5
Concentration! Three	/ 5
Concentration! Four	/ 5
Concentration! Five	/ 5

Concentration!...

_____ 's Scoring Sheet ◀|||

Activity	Score
Concentration! One	/ 5
Concentration! Two	/ 5
Concentration! Three	/ 5
Concentration! Four	/ 5
Concentration! Five	/ 5

World Teachers Press®

Part Two...

In this section, students are required to listen carefully to two lists of items read by the teacher. They then write the missing item from the second list.

The *Item Missing* activities gradually become more complex. Therefore, it is suggested that you work through the sets of activities in the order they are presented. The activities are designed to develop listening and memory skills.

Instructions

⟶ Discuss the fact that exercising or training the mind is similar to training a muscle… success will not be instantaneous, it takes regular practice.

⟶ Use one set of *Item Missing* activities per session. Read both the initial list and the set in brackets, which has one item missing. Read them aloud to the students, slowly, deliberately and clearly, without stressing any particular item. The missing item in each list is in bold type.

⟶ Once you have finished giving each list of items, the students then write the missing item on the scoring sheet on page 32. Give your students time to ponder.

Scoring

⟶ Read the complete set again and supply the answer. Record scores on the scoring sheet on page 32.

⟶ Tell your students that you expect them to be honest—they will be cheating only themselves if, for instance, they score their work incorrectly.

⟶ By filling out their scoring sheets students will be able to monitor their progress, hopefully seeing the improvements they are making when they total their scores each month, assuming you are doing one set each week.

⟶ If improvements are not being made, go back a level and give further practice until the student is ready to move on to a more advanced level.

⟶ NOTE: The scoring sheets are designed so students can monitor their own individual progress—they are not designed to compare scores with anyone else. Please avoid asking the students to call their scores aloud in front of the class unless the students say they are quite comfortable with this. You may collect totals individually instead.

Refer back to instructions for important details on administering and scoring.
Use one set per session. Read the lists of items in each set to the students slowly
and clearly without stressing any particular item.

4 Items – Set One ⬅️||||

1. cardboard **metal** water paper
   (paper, cardboard, water)
2. shouting tranquil noisy **quiet**
   (tranquil, shouting, noisy)
3. **furry** smooth rabbit frog
   (rabbit, smooth, frog)
4. ice glacier desert **hot**
   (desert, glacier, ice)

4 Items – Set Two ⬅️||||

1. **add** multiply divide total
   (multiply, total, divide)
2. knight shield **horse** lance
   (lance, knight, shield)
3. crumpets **fire** toast butter
   (toast, crumpets, butter)
4. lace **frills** fancy dress
   (dress, lace, fancy)

4 Items – Set Three ⬅️||||

1. vegetable meal **snack** fruit
   (vegetable, fruit, meal)
2. stamp **boy** letter air
   (stamp, letter, air)
3. cloud **plane** clock hand
   (clock, cloud, hand)
4. phone bag shovel **sack**
   (shovel, phone, bag)

4 Items – Set Four ⬅️||||

1. mole tunnel **earth** worm
   (worm, mole, tunnel)
2. **hard** difficult easy good
   (easy, good, difficult)
3. beans toast tomato **butter**
   (toast, tomato, beans)
4. icing **jelly** cake cream
   (cake, cream, icing)

4 Items – Set Five ⬅️||||

1. moon **stars** planets sun
   (planets, sun, moon)
2. **tree** branch nest leaf
   (nest, branch, leaf)
3. soil mulch **dirt** mud
   (mulch, soil, mud)
4. seaweed fish shell **water**
   (shell, seaweed, fish)

4 Items – Set Six ⬅️||||

1. nasty kind **funny** mean
   (kind, nasty, mean)
2. pencil **pen** crayon ruler
   (crayon, pencil, ruler)
3. light dark **bright** dull
   (dull, dark, light)
4. **foot** leg hair tooth
   (hair, tooth, leg)

4 Items – Set Seven ⬅️||||

1. **breakfast** lunch tea food
   (food, tea, lunch)
2. tissue cotton **wool** paper
   (cotton, paper, tissue)
3. magazine **book** comic diary
   (comic, magazine, diary)
4. skip sprint walk **jump**
   (sprint, walk, skip)

4 Items – Set Eight ⬅️||||

1. **blunt** sharp bold broad
   (bold, sharp, broad)
2. wheel **brake** door seat
   (door, seat, wheel)
3. **aunt** brother father sister
   (father, sister, brother)
4. envelope card letter **stamp**
   (card, letter, envelope)

Refer back to instructions for important details on administering and scoring. Use one set per session. Read the lists of items in each set to the students slowly and clearly without stressing any particular item.

5 Items – Set One ◀IIII

1. pirate thief robber **police** steal
   (robber, pirate, thief, steal)
2. hat scarf **glove** mitten coat
   (coat, hat, scarf, mitten)
3. door window roof **stairs** fire
   (window, roof, door, fire)
4. giant **castle** hen golden egg
   (giant, egg, golden, hen)

5 Items – Set Two ◀IIII

1. above plane view bird **worm**
   (plane, above, bird, view)
2. **plant** grass flower seed bulb
   (bulb, grass, seed, flower)
3. bird claw beak **nest** eggs
   (eggs, beak, bird, claw)
4. **saw** nail drill hammer screw
   (hammer, screw, drill, nail)

5 Items – Set Three ◀IIII

1. hand finger **thumb** ring bangle
   (finger, bangle, ring, hand)
2. paint brush **canvas** oil artist
   (paint, artist, brush, oil)
3. **smile** laugh think cry talk
   (talk, think, laugh, cry)
4. run fall **trip** ankle break
   (ankle, break, run, fall)

5 Items – Set Four ◀IIII

1. pencil rubber **paper** ruler line
   (ruler, line, pencil, rubber)
2. song **piano** play note read
   (play, note, read, song)
3. **cake** lumpy sweet sugar plums
   (lumpy, sugar, sweet, plums)
4. **hippo** lion tiger moth zebra
   (lion, zebra, moth, tiger)

5 Items – Set Five ◀IIII

1. **ring** diamond lake trees dog
   (diamond, dog, lake, trees)
2. hole bed pillow **book** shadow
   (pillow, shadow, bed, hole)
3. **screen** computer printer picture page
   (printer, page, picture, computer)
4. cake picnic **beach** horse dog
   (picnic, horse, dog, cake)

5 Items – Set Six ◀IIII

1. run jump **bridge** river bank
   (bank, run, river, jump)
2. sky clouds hail **umbrella** trees
   (hail, sky, clouds, trees)
3. juice **orange** glass table thirst
   (table, juice, glass, thirst)
4. **light** lamp bulb read sleep
   (read, lamp, sleep, bulb)

5 Items – Set Seven ◀IIII

1. fly fruit burst **peel** wings
   (burst, fruit, fly, wings)
2. think **head** friend picture telephone
   (friend, telephone, think, picture)
3. jet sky trail **clouds** vapor
   (jet, vapor, trail, sky)
4. sugar candy **red** sweet tooth
   (sweet, candy, sugar, tooth)

5 Items – Set Eight ◀IIII

1. pet rabbit **feed** cage seeds
   (rabbit, seeds, pet, cage)
2. steamer **sea** funnel waves brine
   (funnel, waves, brine, steamer)
3. **address** stamp letter envelope mail
   (letter, mail, envelope, stamp)
4. **desk** teacher play think laugh
   (teacher, laugh, think, play)

Item Missing...

_____'s Scoring Sheet ◀▥

▥▶ **4 Items – Set** _____

1. _____   2. _____   3. _____

4. _____   Total _____

▥▶ **4 Items – Set** _____

1. _____   2. _____   3. _____

4. _____   Total _____

▥▶ **4 Items – Set** _____

1. _____   2. _____   3. _____

4. _____   Total _____

Item Missing...

_____'s Scoring Sheet ◀▥

▥▶ **5 Items – Set** _____

1. _____   2. _____   3. _____

4. _____   Total _____

▥▶ **5 Items – Set** _____

1. _____   2. _____   3. _____

4. _____   Total _____

▥▶ **5 Items – Set** _____

1. _____   2. _____   3. _____

4. _____   Total _____

Part Three...

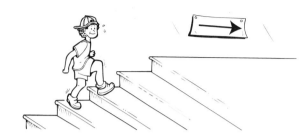

In this section, students are required to listen to a group of digits read by the teacher. They write the same sequence of digits from memory.

Instructions

IIII➡ Discuss the fact that exercising or training the mind is somewhat similar to training a muscle... success will not be instantaneous, it takes regular practice.

IIII➡ Use one set of *Digits Forwards* activities per session. Read one group of digits at a time aloud to the students, slowly and clearly, without stressing any particular digit.

IIII➡ Once you have finished reading each group of digits, the students then write the same sequence of digits from memory on their scoring sheet. Stress that students are to refrain from writing until you have finished reading the group aloud. Give the students time to ponder. Repeat with each group of digits until the set is complete.

IIII➡ A "challenge" from the next level is enjoyed by most students and one is provided for each set.

Scoring

IIII➡ Read each group of digits in the set for students to check their answers. Use the scoring sheet on page 36 to record individual scores. The "challenge" is not recorded in the total on the scoring sheet—this is purely to help develop self-confidence.

IIII➡ Tell your students that you expect them to be honest with themselves—they will be cheating only themselves if they score their work incorrectly, or begin to write the number before being told.

IIII➡ By filling out their scoring sheets students will be able to monitor their progress and hopefully see the improvements they are making when they total their scores each month, assuming you are doing these each week.

IIII➡ If improvements are not being made, go back a level and give further practice until the student is ready to move on to a more advanced level.

IIII➡ NOTE: The scoring sheet on page 36 is designed so students can monitor their own individual progress—they are not designed to compare scores with anyone else. Please avoid asking the students to call their scores aloud in front of the class, unless the students say they are quite comfortable with this. You may collect totals individually instead.

Refer back to instructions for important details on administering and scoring. Use one set per session. Read the groups of digits in each set to the students slowly and clearly without stressing any particular item.

5 Digits – Set One ◀‖‖

98556	41875	35697
42885	25864	35981

Challenge: 672958

5 Digits – Set Two ◀‖‖

78741	01408	90827
40189	56714	30583

Challenge: 779632

5 Digits – Set Three ◀‖‖

94278	25085	47195
25874	60908	43986

Challenge: 791346

5 Digits – Set Four ◀‖‖

69257	86425	42958
43786	30918	80524

Challenge: 694877

5 Digits – Set Five ◀‖‖

46125	98602	02877
37584	08395	85847

Challenge: 378601

5 Digits – Set Six ◀‖‖

47147	09765	35956
40186	73589	45811

Challenge: 316497

5 Digits – Set Seven ◀‖‖

25631	25954	20578
86259	32587	10256

Challenge: 362598

5 Digits – Set Eight ◀‖‖

56897	20568	50142
89356	25874	25968

Challenge: 021563

5 Digits – Set Nine ◀‖‖

32569	52147	85236
85471	32569	85412

Challenge: 325698

5 Digits – Set Ten ◀‖‖

02156	32580	12405
95201	30258	45201

Challenge: 036580

5 Digits – Set Eleven ◀‖‖

25987	25841	36589
98563	78541	25896

Challenge: 032569

5 Digits – Set Twelve ◀‖‖

25894	23654	12548
35698	56325	14528

Challenge: 236589

Refer back to instructions for important details on administering and scoring.
Use one set per session. Read the groups of digits in each set to the students
slowly and clearly without stressing any particular item.

6 Digits – Set One ◀‖‖

574198   689174   159154
425879   574578   357195
Challenge: 5789741

6 Digits – Set Two ◀‖‖

541287   481267   656870
085249   357149   251034
Challenge: 5871353

6 Digits – Set Three ◀‖‖

587432   971302   458760
249781   203078   774108
Challenge: 2719587

6 Digits – Set Four ◀‖‖

862579   487503   461298
250548   306892   515792
Challenge: 5473260

6 Digits – Set Five ◀‖‖

587900   963782   306856
874821   697823   594071
Challenge: 7756205

6 Digits – Set Six ◀‖‖

212057   515758   842978
018706   971982   528045
Challenge: 2016841

6 Digits – Set Seven ◀‖‖

989561   457891   024108
762551   107935   406528
Challenge: 6639375

6 Digits – Set Eight ◀‖‖

565985   101537   852748
425896   303217   987745
Challenge: 3012459

6 Digits – Set Nine ◀‖‖

568544   201487   323690
520158   976458   102138
Challenge: 3120571

6 Digits – Set Ten ◀‖‖

569837   195874   205191
508765   040783   313794
Challenge: 3125647

6 Digits – Set Eleven ◀‖‖

798756   848752   281739
342195   579848   134679
Challenge: 6469820

6 Digits – Set Twelve ◀‖‖

805132   917382   208139
604379   502841   325874
Challenge: 6659801

Digits Forwards...

_____'s Scoring Sheet ◀||||

▶ **5 Digits – Set** _____

_____   _____   _____   _____

_____   Challenge _____   Total _____

▶ **5 Digits – Set** _____

_____   _____   _____   _____

_____   Challenge _____   Total _____

▶ **5 Digits – Set** _____

_____   _____   _____   _____

_____   Challenge _____   Total _____

Digits Forwards...

_____'s Scoring Sheet ◀||||

▶ **6 Digits – Set** _____

_____   _____   _____   _____

_____   Challenge _____   Total _____

▶ **6 Digits – Set** _____

_____   _____   _____   _____

_____   Challenge _____   Total _____

▶ **6 Digits – Set** _____

_____   _____   _____   _____

_____   Challenge _____   Total _____

Part Four...

In this section, students are required to listen to a group of digits read by the teacher. They write the same sequence of digits from memory in reverse order.

Instructions

▮➤ Use one set of *Digits Backwards* activities per session. Read one group of digits at a time aloud to the students slowly and clearly, without stressing any particular digit.

▮➤ Once you have finished reading each group of digits, the students then write the same sequence of digits from memory on their scoring sheet in reverse order. Stress that the students are to refrain from writing until you have finished reading the group aloud.

▮➤ Students should not write the digits down from right to left on their page, or write them from left to right and then rewrite them reversed; but should hold the sequence in their memory and turn it around. For example, if the sequence given is 45678, they should remember it, turn it around and write 87654.

▮➤ It should be stressed to the students that they are training their minds, in essence, to memorize and manipulate items. If they don't hold the sequence in their memory and turn it around before writing it down they are not training themselves for subsequent sets. Honesty here sets them up for more difficult future sets. Honesty is the best policy.

▮➤ A "challenge" from the next level, is enjoyed by most students and one is provided for each set.

Scoring

▮➤ Read each group of digits in reverse order for students to check their answers. Use the scoring sheet on page 40 to record individual scores. The "challenge" is not recorded in the total on the scoring sheet—this is purely to help develop self-confidence.

▮➤ By filling out their scoring sheets students will be able to monitor their progress and hopefully see the improvements they are making when they total their scores each month, assuming you are doing these each week.

▮➤ If improvements are not being made, go back a level and give further practice until the student is ready to move on to a more advanced level.

▮➤ NOTE: The scoring sheet on page 40 is designed so students can monitor their own individual progress—they are not designed to compare scores with anyone else. Please avoid asking the students to call their scores aloud in front of the class, unless the students say they are quite comfortable with this. You may collect totals individually instead.

Refer back to instructions for important details on administering and scoring. Use one set per session. Read the groups of digits in each set to the students slowly and clearly without stressing any particular item.

4 Digits – Set One ◀IIII

5495	4189	1205
6359	1027	6894

Challenge: 87420

4 Digits – Set Two ◀IIII

5841	7489	1207
3219	2983	1097

Challenge: 10176

4 Digits – Set Three ◀IIII

6857	5294	1249
2541	2869	5457

Challenge: 15874

4 Digits – Set Four ◀IIII

6535	4297	5120
4871	3021	2278

Challenge: 46921

4 Digits – Set Five ◀IIII

9645	5114	7647
2028	6394	4870

Challenge: 69509

4 Digits – Set Six ◀IIII

1789	5541	5026
2360	7438	8091

Challenge: 92340

4 Digits – Set Seven ◀IIII

2563	2587	4526
9856	8547	6253

Challenge: 32569

4 Digits – Set Eight ◀IIII

8457	6254	2569
5469	1258	3652

Challenge: 30569

4 Digits – Set Nine ◀IIII

8547	6325	9856
2541	2365	8547

Challenge: 03256

4 Digits – Set Ten ◀IIII

8214	6320	9658
0256	3021	5201

Challenge: 69885

4 Digits – Set Eleven ◀IIII

4210	3620	8521
9521	3204	6201

Challenge: 95201

4 Digits – Set Twelve ◀IIII

5536	2210	9658
8854	2539	1253

Challenge: 32056

World Teachers Press®

Digits Backwards ⬅▪▪▪

Refer back to instructions for important details on administering and scoring.
Use one set per session. Read the groups of digits in each set to the students
slowly and clearly without stressing any particular item.

5 Digits – Set One ⬅▪▪▪
59302	57810	49357
80249	54870	30971

Challenge: 798214

5 Digits – Set Two ⬅▪▪▪
10253	75109	46268
20497	15297	12068

Challenge: 975280

5 Digits – Set Three ⬅▪▪▪
79415	45269	10287
84578	41029	54781

Challenge: 578544

5 Digits – Set Four ⬅▪▪▪
46527	87103	20542
05897	24583	78710

Challenge: 353987

5 Digits – Set Five ⬅▪▪▪
65258	41098	78903
87950	20596	65471

Challenge: 636811

5 Digits – Set Six ⬅▪▪▪
96369	58512	42871
20287	46965	15170

Challenge: 753581

5 Digits – Set Seven ⬅▪▪▪
98561	36957	42587
58712	96840	52871

Challenge: 369832

5 Digits – Set Eight ⬅▪▪▪
30357	50578	20247
52089	51451	50578

Challenge: 699301

5 Digits – Set Nine ⬅▪▪▪
65985	10254	87853
31538	58424	89552

Challenge: 989252

5 Digits – Set Ten ⬅▪▪▪
58758	65587	22548
13246	58274	21247

Challenge: 417448

5 Digits – Set Eleven ⬅▪▪▪
69615	30249	15418
46137	20809	39713

Challenge: 133497

5 Digits – Set Twelve ⬅▪▪▪
87492	54487	50389
78720	76598	08476

Challenge: 814370

Digits Backwards...

_____'s Scoring Sheet ◀

➡ **4 Digits – Set** _____

_____   _____   _____   _____

_____   Challenge _____   Total _____

➡ **4 Digits – Set** _____

_____   _____   _____   _____

_____   Challenge _____   Total _____

➡ **4 Digits – Set** _____

_____   _____   _____   _____

_____   Challenge _____   Total _____

Digits Backwards...

_____'s Scoring Sheet ◀

➡ **5 Digits – Set** _____

_____   _____   _____   _____

_____   Challenge _____   Total _____

➡ **5 Digits – Set** _____

_____   _____   _____   _____

_____   Challenge _____   Total _____

➡ **5 Digits – Set** _____

_____   _____   _____   _____

_____   Challenge _____   Total _____

World Teachers Press®